This Book Belongs To:

D1081987

Name: _____

Email: _____

Socials: _____

_____

_____

_____

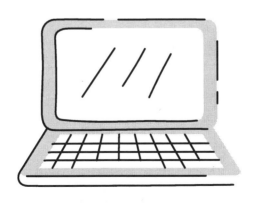

About Me!

What do I want to achieve?
Do I want to meet new friends? Turn this into a career? Raise money for charity?

_____

_____

_____

Who I admire & Why!
These are the creators that I admire most and what I like best about them!

_____

_____

_____

_____

CREATOR MILESTONES!

THESE ARE THE IMPORTANT DATES TO REMEMBER & CELEBRATE!

Creator Milestones!

These are the important dates to remember & celebrate!

Content Ideas!

These are some things I would like to do on my platform!

_____

_____

_____

_____

_____

_____

_____

_____

_____

_____

_____

_____

_____

_____

_____

_____

_____

_____

_____

_____

_____

_____

_____

Content Ideas!

These are some things I would like to do on my platform!

_____

_____

_____

_____

_____

_____

_____

_____

_____

_____

_____

_____

_____

_____

_____

_____

_____

_____

_____

_____

_____

_____

_____

Weekly Planner!

Week Beginning: _____

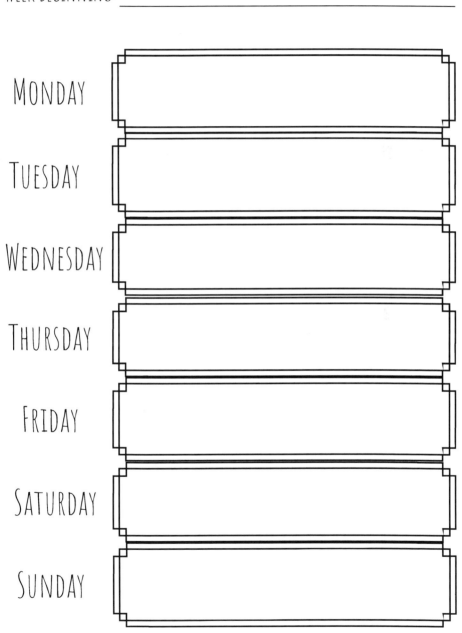

Monday

Tuesday

Wednesday

Thursday

Friday

Saturday

Sunday

Priority Tasks

Little Extras

Goals For This Week

CONTENT NOTES!

Weekly Planner!

Week Beginning: _____

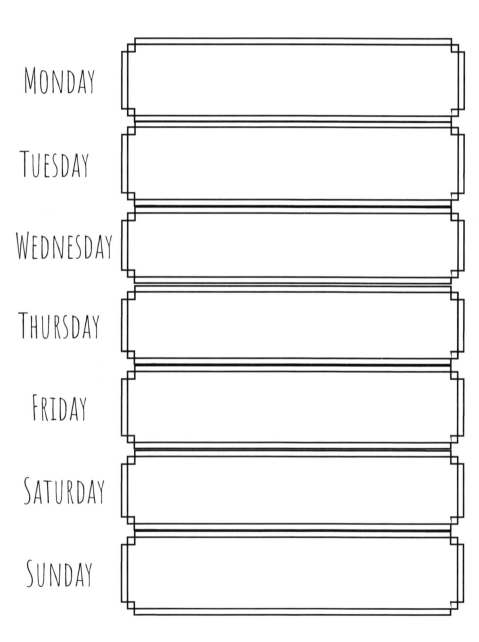

Monday

Tuesday

Wednesday

Thursday

Friday

Saturday

Sunday

Priority Tasks

Little Extras

Goals For This Week

CONTENT NOTES!

Weekly Planner!

Week Beginning: _____

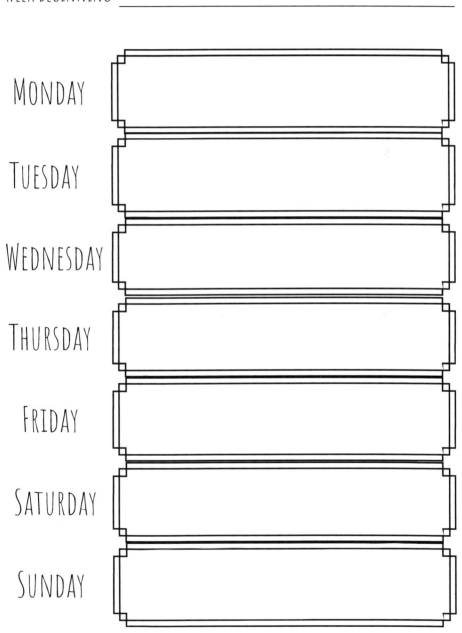

Monday

Tuesday

Wednesday

Thursday

Friday

Saturday

Sunday

Priority Tasks

Little Extras

Goals For This Week

Content notes!

Weekly Planner!

Week Beginning: _____

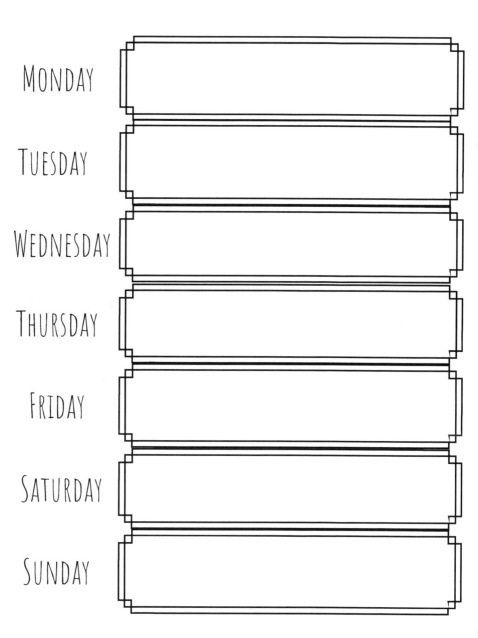

Monday

Tuesday

Wednesday

Thursday

Friday

Saturday

Sunday

Priority Tasks

Little Extras

Goals For This Week

Content notes!

Weekly Planner!

Week Beginning: _____

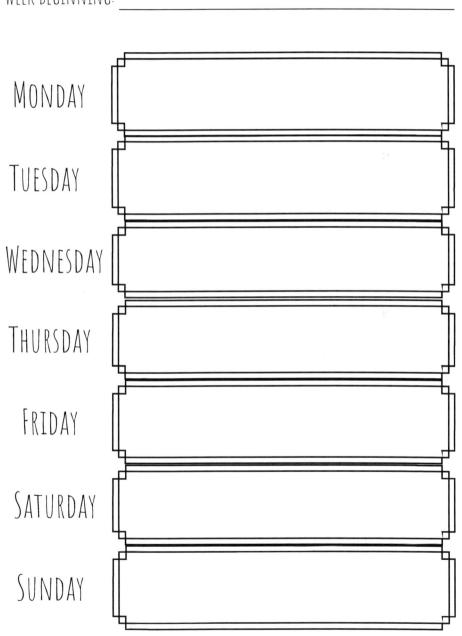

Monday

Tuesday

Wednesday

Thursday

Friday

Saturday

Sunday

Priority Tasks

Little Extras

Goals For This Week

CONTENT NOTES!

Weekly Planner!

Week Beginning: _____

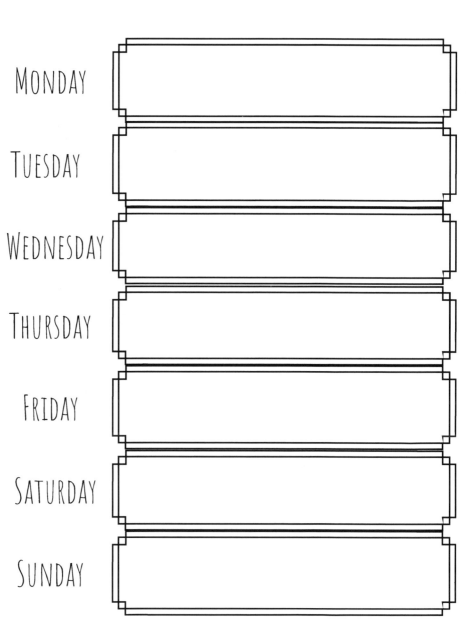

Monday

Tuesday

Wednesday

Thursday

Friday

Saturday

Sunday

Priority Tasks

Little Extras

Goals For This Week

CONTENT NOTES!

Weekly Planner!

Week Beginning: _____

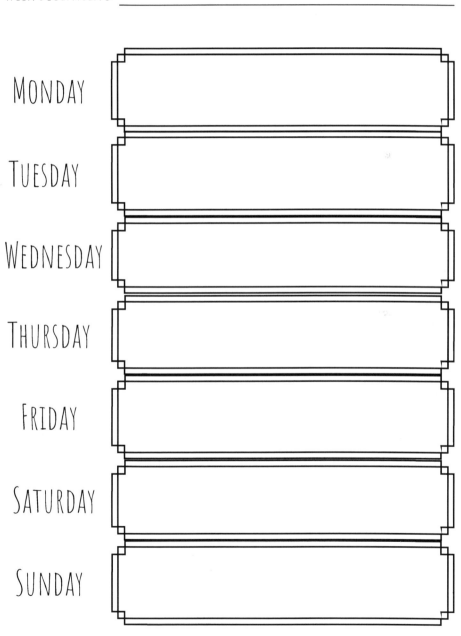

Monday

Tuesday

Wednesday

Thursday

Friday

Saturday

Sunday

Priority Tasks

Little Extras

Goals For This Week

Content notes!

Weekly Planner!

Week Beginning: _____

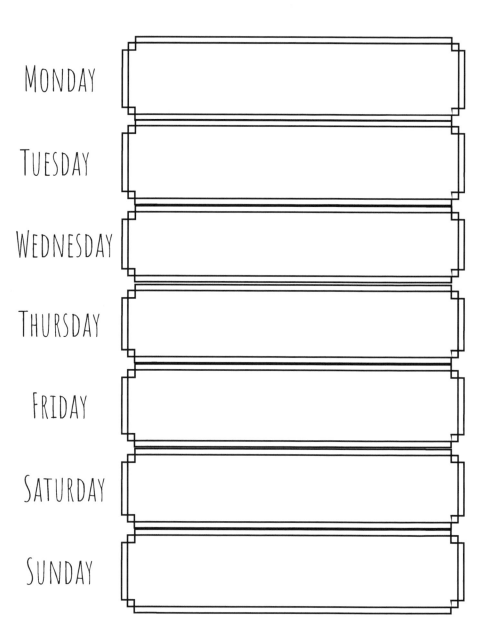

Monday

Tuesday

Wednesday

Thursday

Friday

Saturday

Sunday

Priority Tasks

Little Extras

Goals For This Week

CONTENT NOTES!

_____

_____

_____

_____

_____

_____

_____

_____

_____

_____

_____

_____

_____

_____

_____

_____

_____

_____

_____

_____

Weekly Planner!

Week Beginning: _____

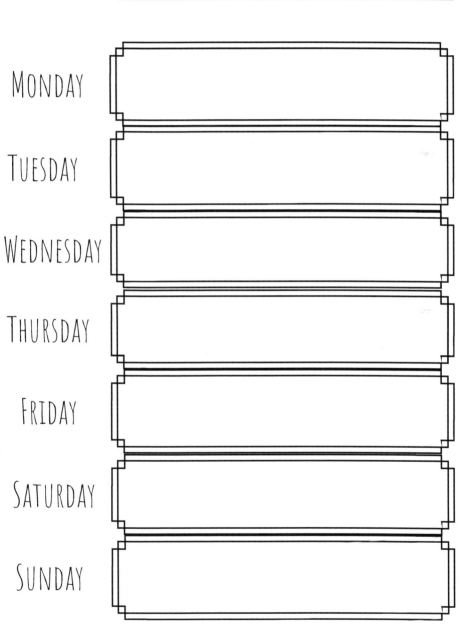

Monday

Tuesday

Wednesday

Thursday

Friday

Saturday

Sunday

Priority Tasks

Little Extras

Goals For This Week

CONTENT NOTES!

_____
_____
_____
_____
_____
_____
_____
_____
_____
_____
_____
_____
_____
_____
_____
_____
_____
_____
_____
_____

Weekly Planner!

Week Beginning: _____

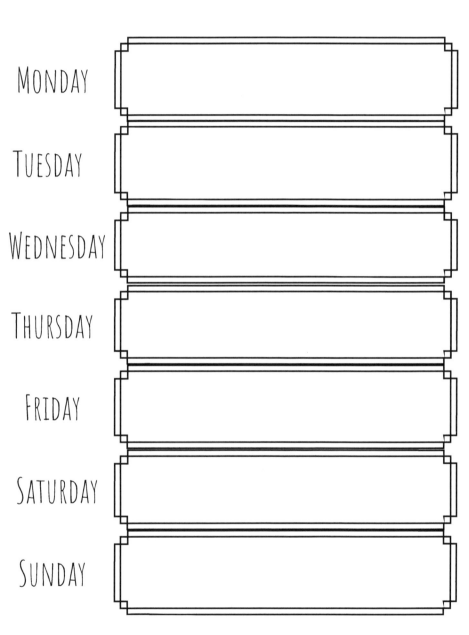

Monday

Tuesday

Wednesday

Thursday

Friday

Saturday

Sunday

Priority Tasks

Little Extras

Goals For This Week

CONTENT NOTES!

Weekly Planner!

Week Beginning: _____

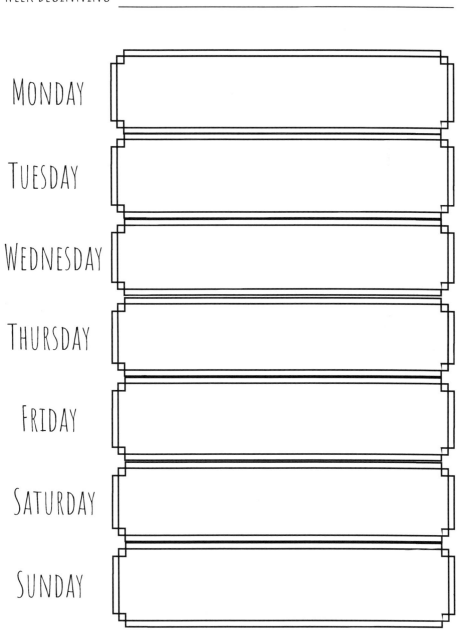

Monday

Tuesday

Wednesday

Thursday

Friday

Saturday

Sunday

Priority Tasks

Little Extras

Goals For This Week

CONTENT NOTES!

Weekly Planner!

Week Beginning: _____

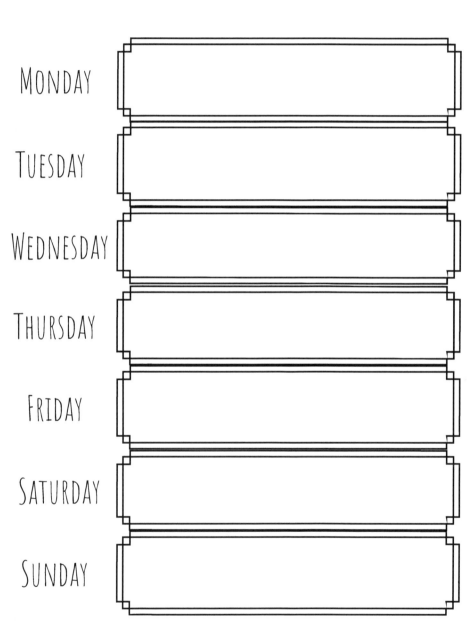

Monday

Tuesday

Wednesday

Thursday

Friday

Saturday

Sunday

Priority Tasks

Little Extras

Goals For This Week

CONTENT NOTES!

Weekly Planner!

Week Beginning: _____

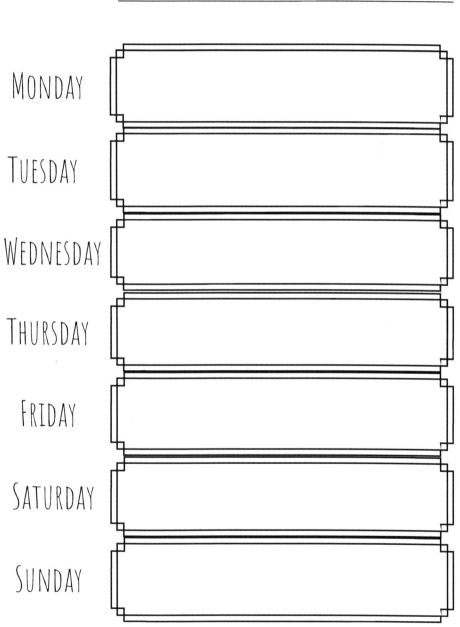

Monday

Tuesday

Wednesday

Thursday

Friday

Saturday

Sunday

Priority Tasks

Little Extras

Goals For This Week

CONTENT NOTES!

Weekly Planner!

Week Beginning: _____

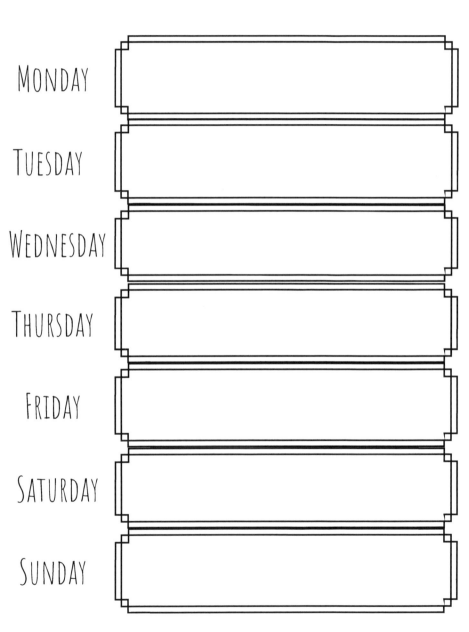

Monday

Tuesday

Wednesday

Thursday

Friday

Saturday

Sunday

Priority Tasks

Little Extras

Goals For This Week

CONTENT NOTES!

Weekly Planner!

Week Beginning: _____

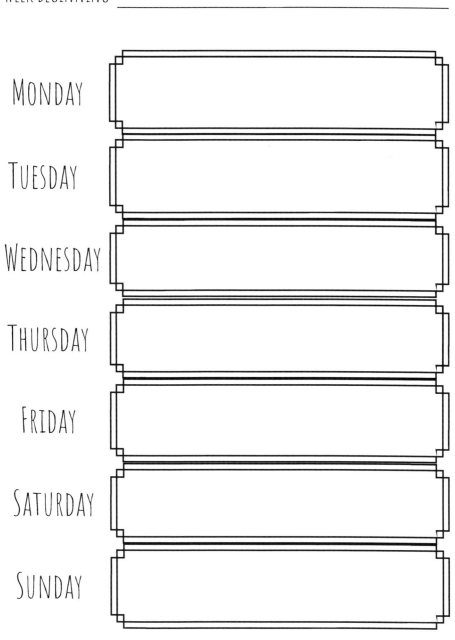

Monday

Tuesday

Wednesday

Thursday

Friday

Saturday

Sunday

Priority Tasks

Little Extras

Goals For This Week

CONTENT NOTES!

Weekly Planner!

Week Beginning: _____

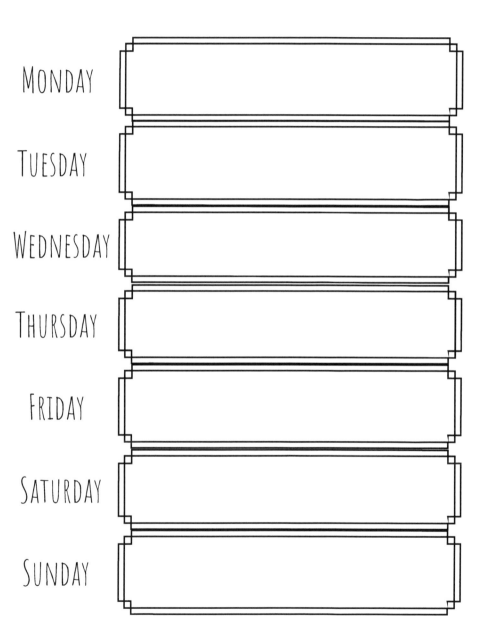

Monday

Tuesday

Wednesday

Thursday

Friday

Saturday

Sunday

Priority Tasks

Little Extras

Goals For This Week

CONTENT NOTES!

Weekly Planner!

Week Beginning: _____

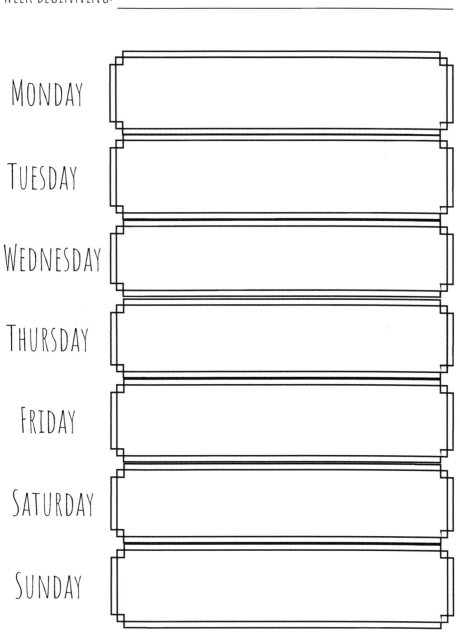

Monday

Tuesday

Wednesday

Thursday

Friday

Saturday

Sunday

Priority Tasks

Little Extras

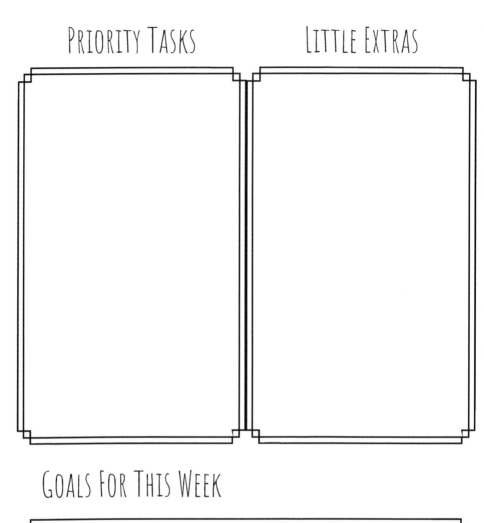

Goals For This Week

Content notes!

Weekly Planner!

Week Beginning: _____

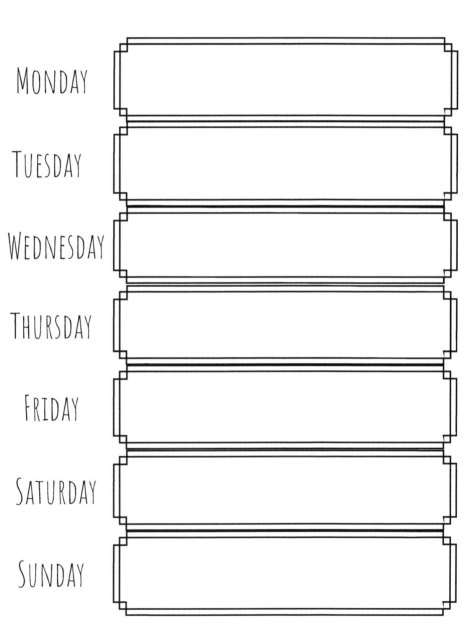

Monday

Tuesday

Wednesday

Thursday

Friday

Saturday

Sunday

Priority Tasks

Little Extras

Goals For This Week

Content notes!

Weekly Planner!

Week Beginning: _____

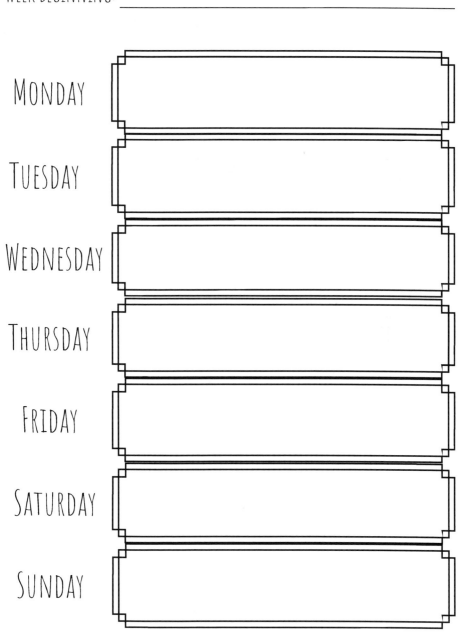

Monday

Tuesday

Wednesday

Thursday

Friday

Saturday

Sunday

Priority Tasks

Little Extras

Goals For This Week

CONTENT NOTES!

Weekly Planner!

Week Beginning: _____

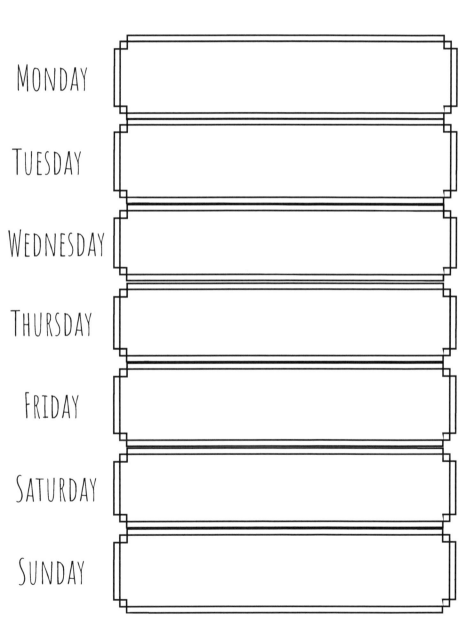

Monday

Tuesday

Wednesday

Thursday

Friday

Saturday

Sunday

Priority Tasks

Little Extras

Goals For This Week

CONTENT NOTES!

Weekly Planner!

Week Beginning: _____

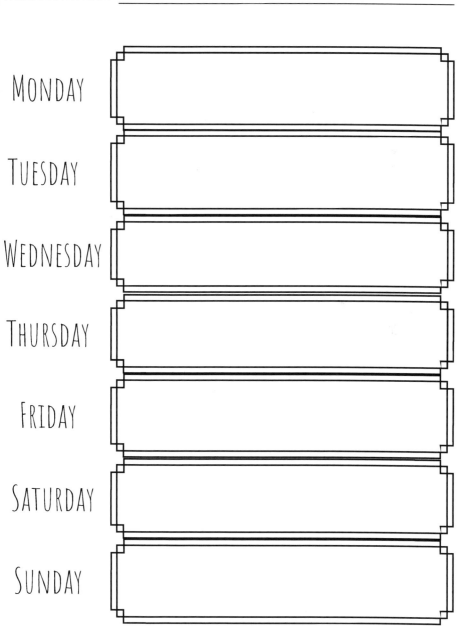

Monday

Tuesday

Wednesday

Thursday

Friday

Saturday

Sunday

Priority Tasks

Little Extras

Goals For This Week

CONTENT NOTES!

Weekly Planner!

Week Beginning: _____

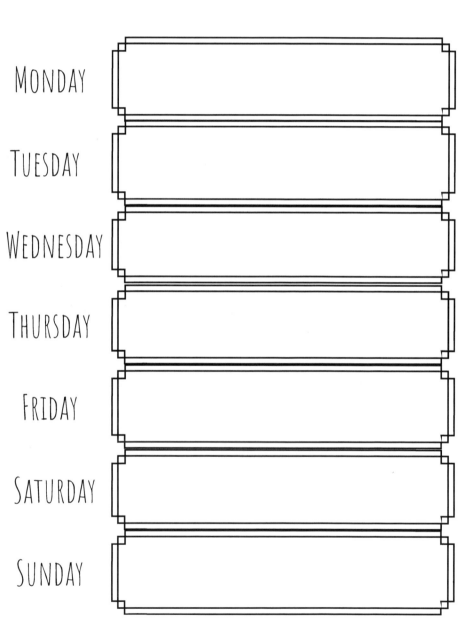

Monday

Tuesday

Wednesday

Thursday

Friday

Saturday

Sunday

Priority Tasks

Little Extras

Goals For This Week

CONTENT NOTES!

Weekly Planner!

Week Beginning: _____

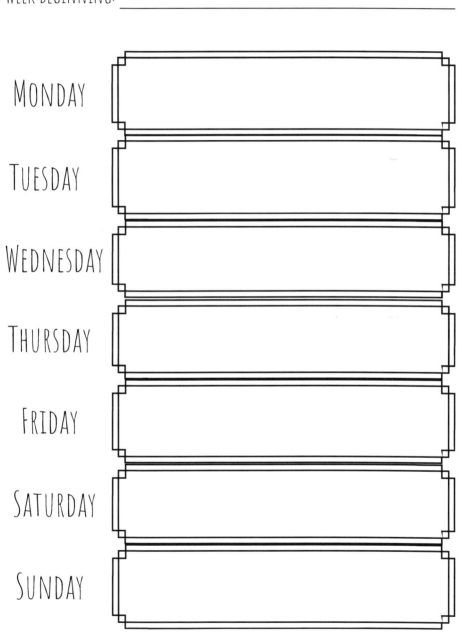

Monday

Tuesday

Wednesday

Thursday

Friday

Saturday

Sunday

Priority Tasks

Little Extras

Goals For This Week

Content notes!

Weekly Planner!

Week Beginning: _____

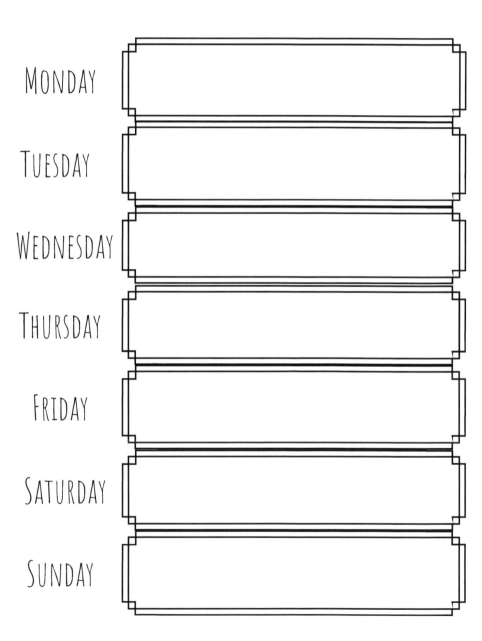

Monday

Tuesday

Wednesday

Thursday

Friday

Saturday

Sunday

Priority Tasks

Little Extras

Goals For This Week

CONTENT NOTES!

Weekly Planner!

Week Beginning: _____

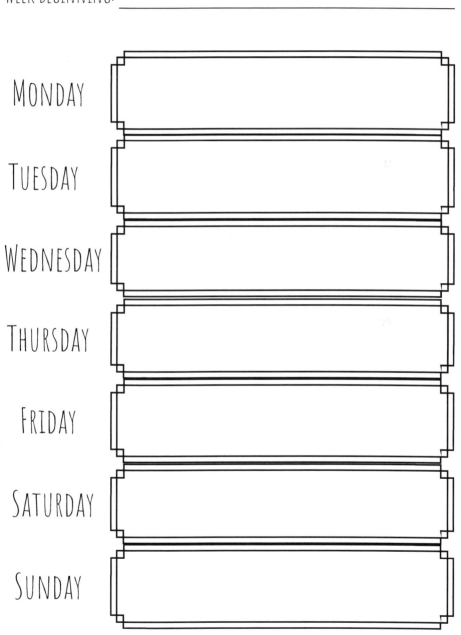

Monday

Tuesday

Wednesday

Thursday

Friday

Saturday

Sunday

Priority Tasks

Little Extras

Goals For This Week

CONTENT NOTES!

Weekly Planner!

Week Beginning: _____

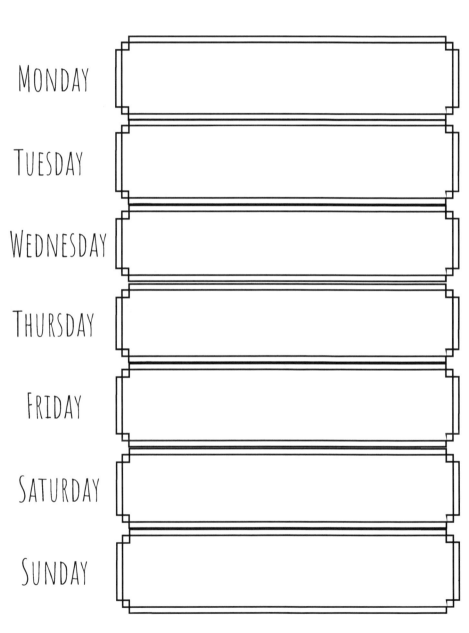

Monday

Tuesday

Wednesday

Thursday

Friday

Saturday

Sunday

Priority Tasks

Little Extras

Goals For This Week

Content notes!

Weekly Planner!

Week Beginning: _____

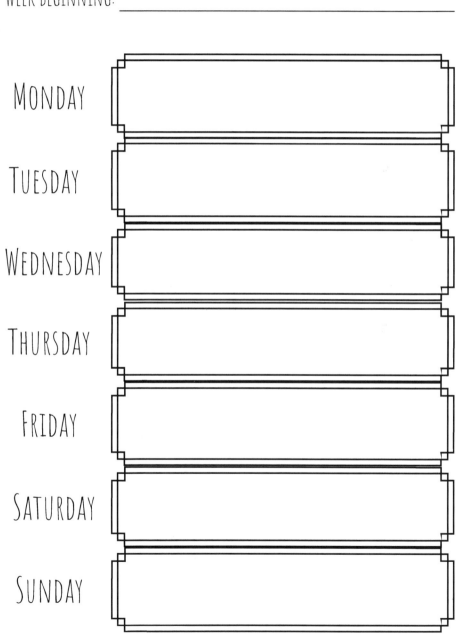

Monday

Tuesday

Wednesday

Thursday

Friday

Saturday

Sunday

Priority Tasks

Little Extras

Goals For This Week

CONTENT NOTES!

Weekly Planner!

Week Beginning: _____

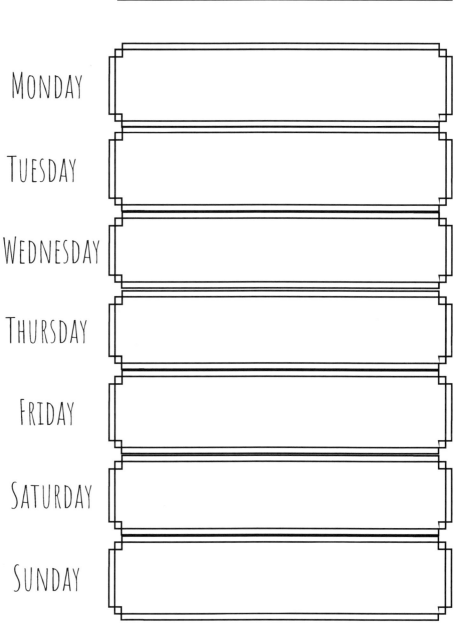

Monday

Tuesday

Wednesday

Thursday

Friday

Saturday

Sunday

Priority Tasks

Little Extras

Goals For This Week

CONTENT NOTES!

Weekly Planner!

Week Beginning: _____

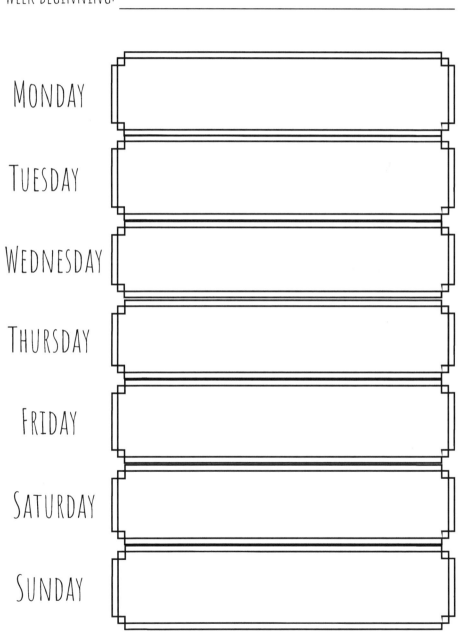

Monday

Tuesday

Wednesday

Thursday

Friday

Saturday

Sunday

Priority Tasks

Little Extras

Goals For This Week

Content notes!

_____
_____
_____
_____
_____
_____
_____
_____
_____
_____
_____
_____
_____
_____
_____
_____
_____
_____
_____
_____
_____
_____

Weekly Planner!

Week Beginning: _____

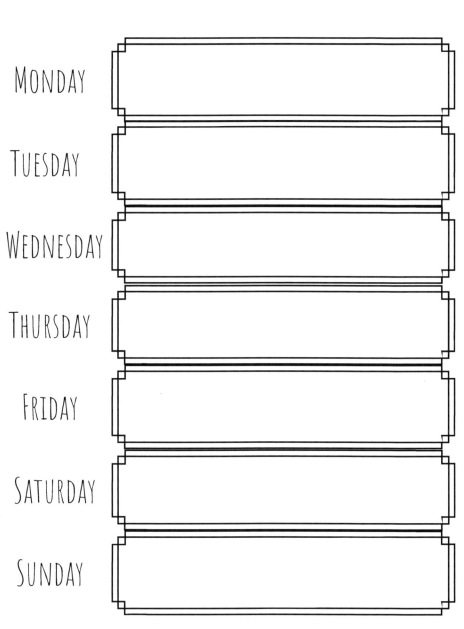

Monday

Tuesday

Wednesday

Thursday

Friday

Saturday

Sunday

Priority Tasks

Little Extras

Goals For This Week

CONTENT NOTES!

Weekly Planner!

Week Beginning: _____

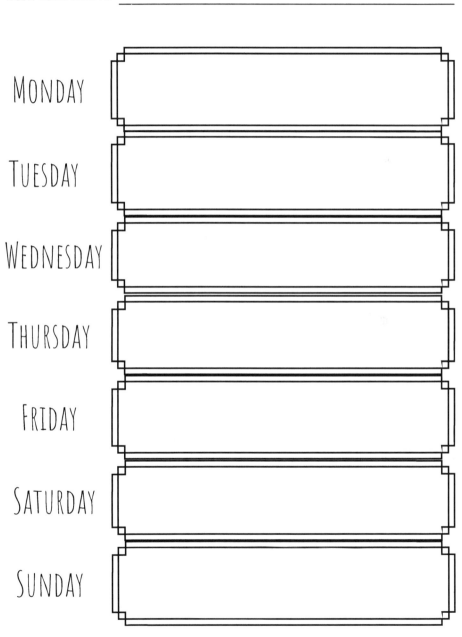

Monday

Tuesday

Wednesday

Thursday

Friday

Saturday

Sunday

Priority Tasks

Little Extras

Goals For This Week

CONTENT NOTES!

Weekly Planner!

Week Beginning: _____

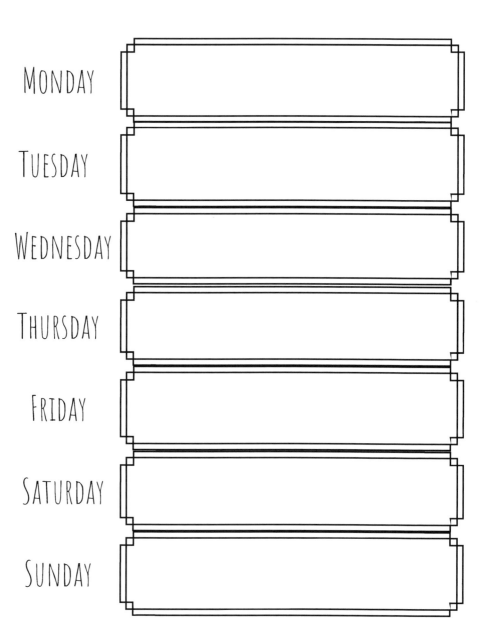

Monday

Tuesday

Wednesday

Thursday

Friday

Saturday

Sunday

Priority Tasks

Little Extras

Goals For This Week

CONTENT NOTES!

Weekly Planner!

Week Beginning: _____

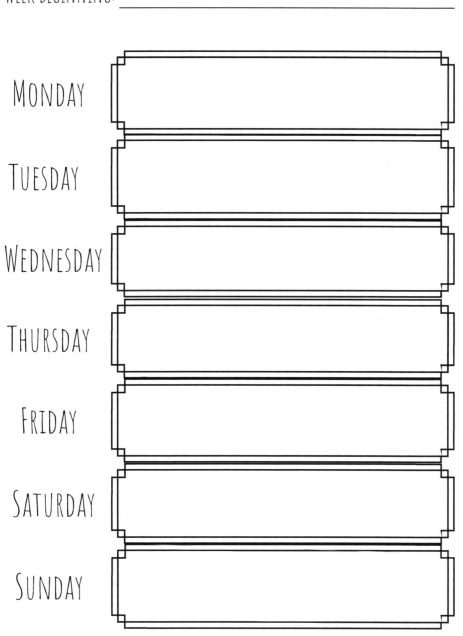

Monday

Tuesday

Wednesday

Thursday

Friday

Saturday

Sunday

Priority Tasks

Little Extras

Goals For This Week

CONTENT NOTES!

Weekly Planner!

Week Beginning: _____

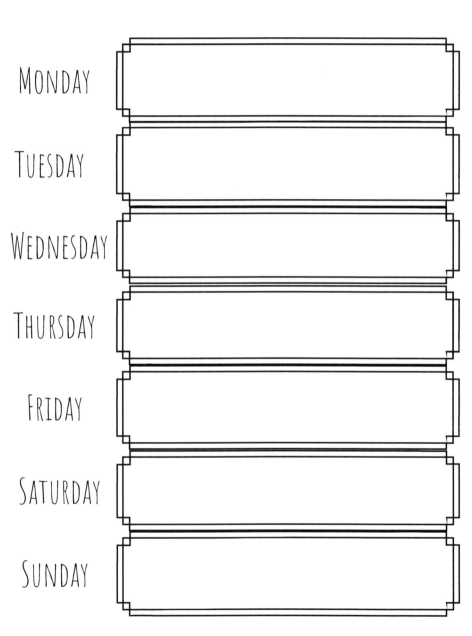

Monday

Tuesday

Wednesday

Thursday

Friday

Saturday

Sunday

Priority Tasks

Little Extras

Goals For This Week

CONTENT NOTES!

Weekly Planner!

Week Beginning: _____

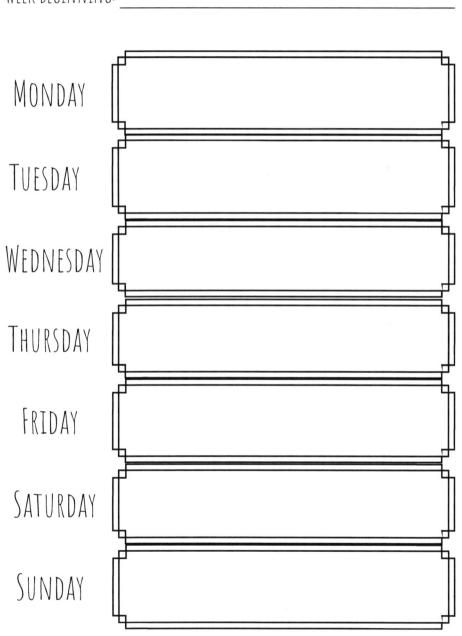

Monday

Tuesday

Wednesday

Thursday

Friday

Saturday

Sunday

Priority Tasks

Little Extras

Goals For This Week

CONTENT NOTES!

Weekly Planner!

Week Beginning: _____

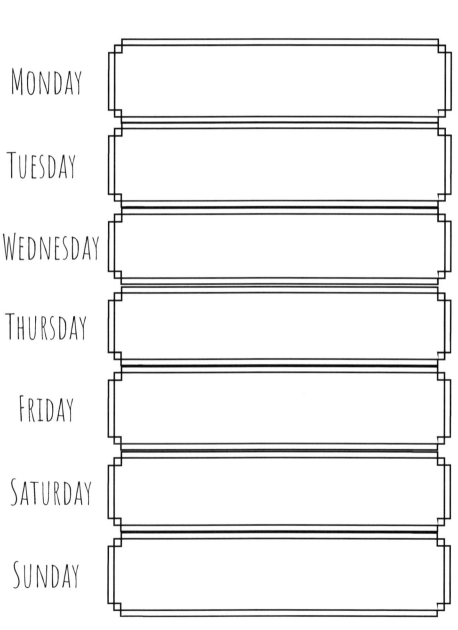

Monday

Tuesday

Wednesday

Thursday

Friday

Saturday

Sunday

Priority Tasks

Little Extras

Goals For This Week

CONTENT NOTES!

Weekly Planner!

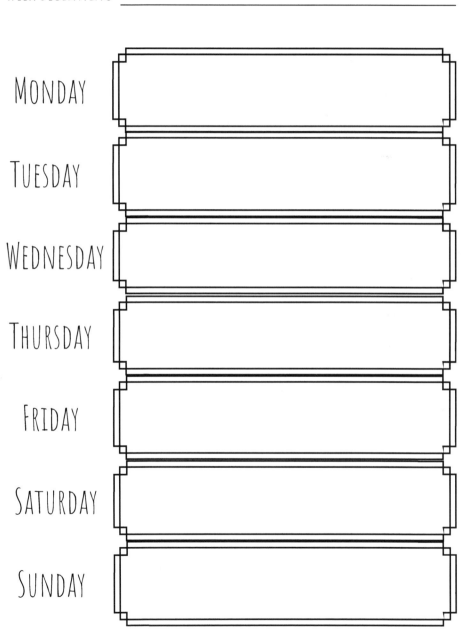

Monday

Tuesday

Wednesday

Thursday

Friday

Saturday

Sunday

Priority Tasks

Little Extras

Goals For This Week

CONTENT NOTES!

Weekly Planner!

Week Beginning: _____

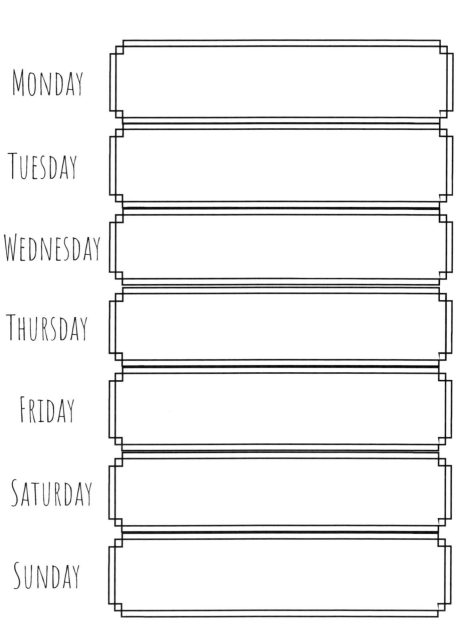

Monday

Tuesday

Wednesday

Thursday

Friday

Saturday

Sunday

Priority Tasks

Little Extras

Goals For This Week

CONTENT NOTES!

Weekly Planner!

Week Beginning: _____

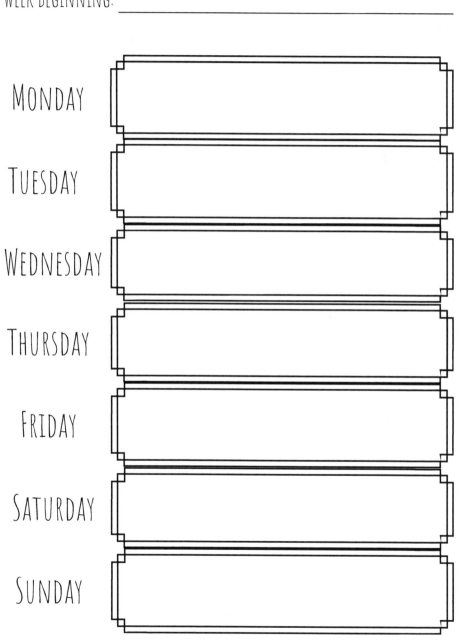

Monday

Tuesday

Wednesday

Thursday

Friday

Saturday

Sunday

Priority Tasks

Little Extras

Goals For This Week

CONTENT NOTES!

Weekly Planner!

Week Beginning: _____

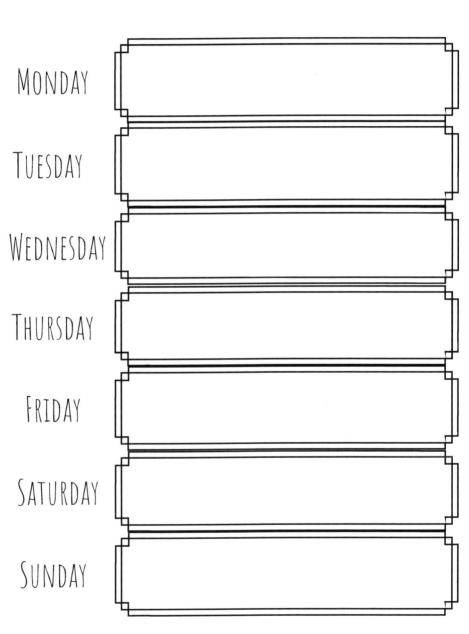

Monday

Tuesday

Wednesday

Thursday

Friday

Saturday

Sunday

Priority Tasks

Little Extras

Goals For This Week

CONTENT NOTES!

Weekly Planner!

Week Beginning: _____

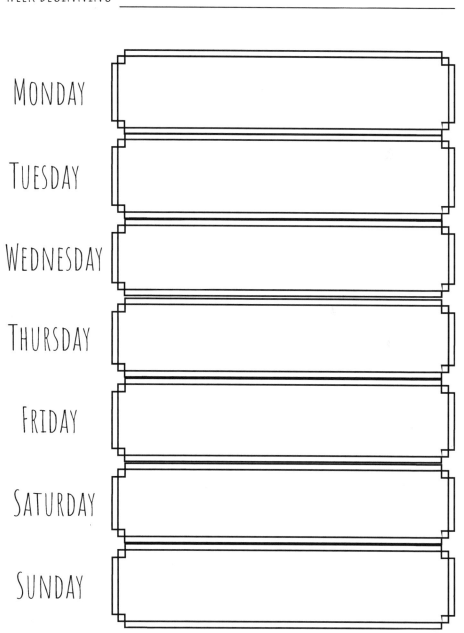

Monday

Tuesday

Wednesday

Thursday

Friday

Saturday

Sunday

Priority Tasks

Little Extras

Goals For This Week

CONTENT NOTES!

Weekly Planner!

Week Beginning: _____

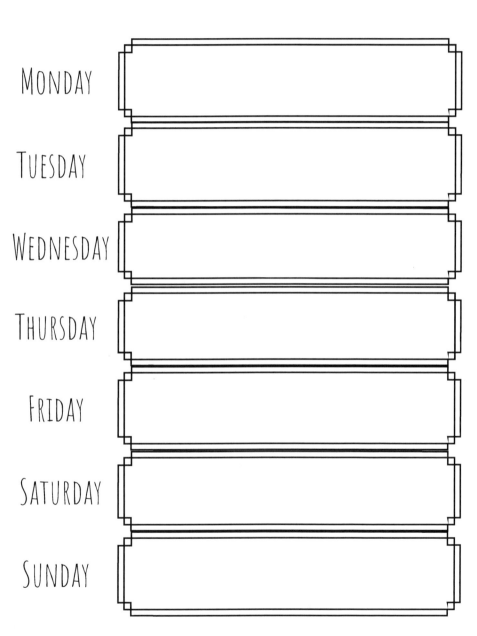

Monday

Tuesday

Wednesday

Thursday

Friday

Saturday

Sunday

Priority Tasks

Little Extras

Goals For This Week

CONTENT NOTES!

Weekly Planner!

Week Beginning: _____

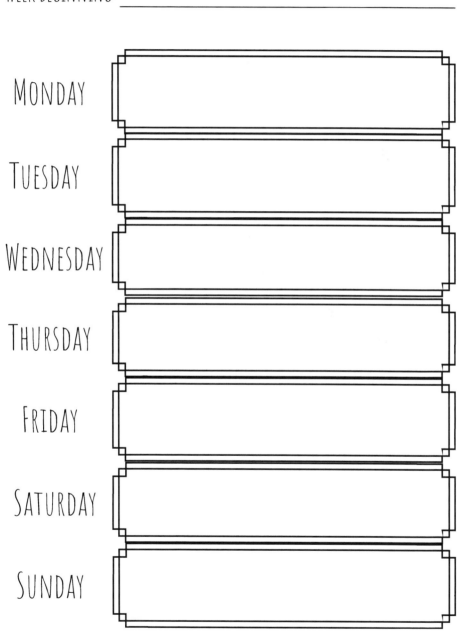

Monday

Tuesday

Wednesday

Thursday

Friday

Saturday

Sunday

Priority Tasks

Little Extras

Goals For This Week

Content notes!

Weekly Planner!

Week Beginning: _____

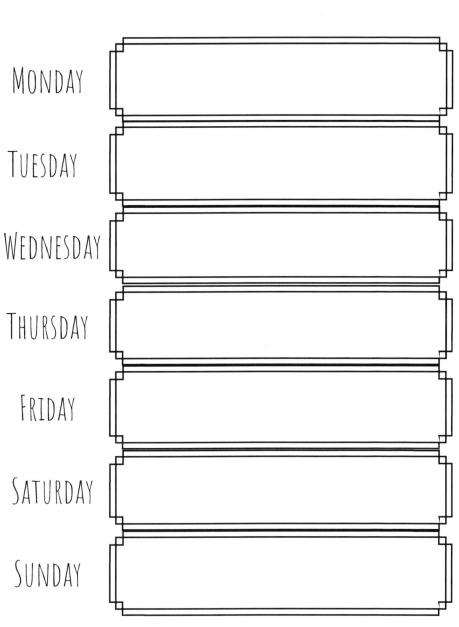

Monday

Tuesday

Wednesday

Thursday

Friday

Saturday

Sunday

Priority Tasks

Little Extras

Goals For This Week

CONTENT NOTES!

Weekly Planner!

Week Beginning: _____

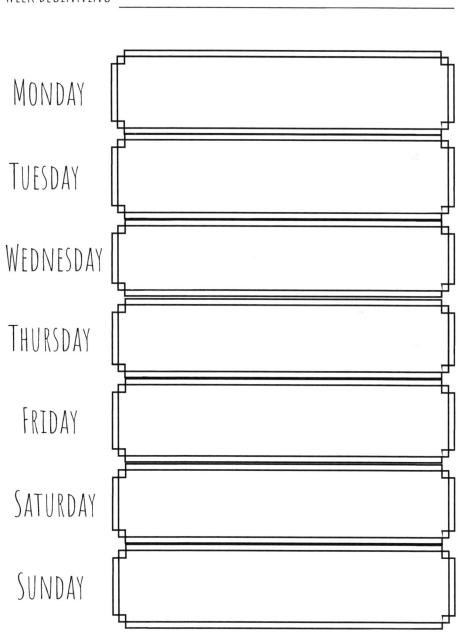

Monday

Tuesday

Wednesday

Thursday

Friday

Saturday

Sunday

Priority Tasks

Little Extras

Goals For This Week

CONTENT NOTES!

Weekly Planner!

Week Beginning: _____

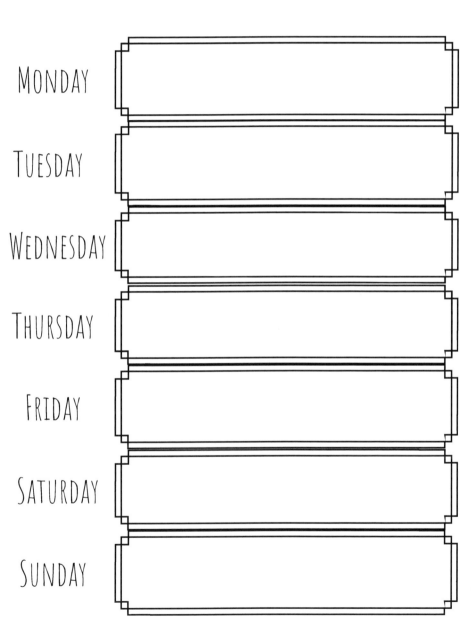

Monday

Tuesday

Wednesday

Thursday

Friday

Saturday

Sunday

Priority Tasks

Little Extras

Goals For This Week

CONTENT NOTES!

Weekly Planner!

Week Beginning: _____

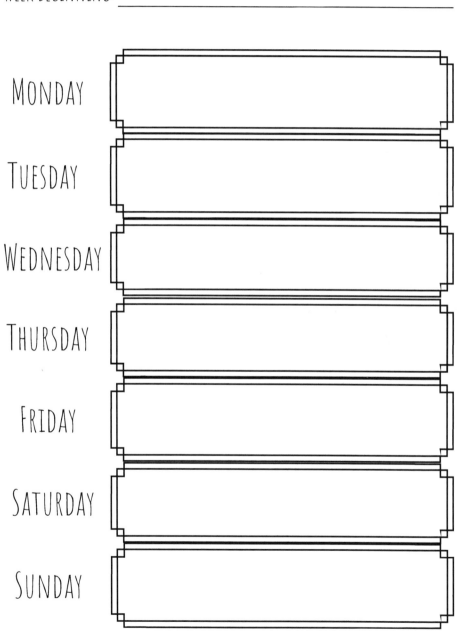

Monday

Tuesday

Wednesday

Thursday

Friday

Saturday

Sunday

Priority Tasks

Little Extras

Goals For This Week

CONTENT NOTES!

Weekly Planner!

Week Beginning: _____

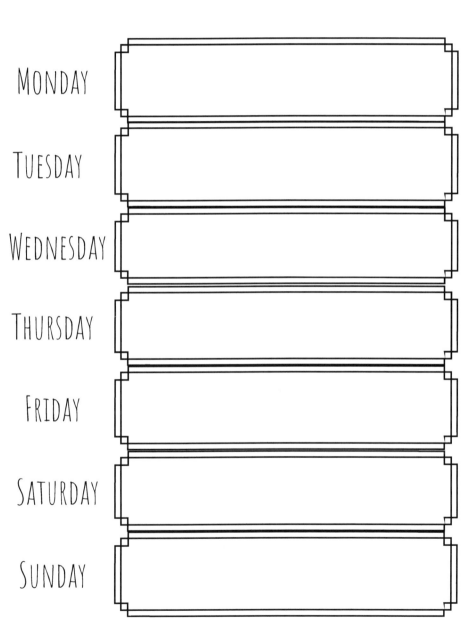

Monday

Tuesday

Wednesday

Thursday

Friday

Saturday

Sunday

Priority Tasks

Little Extras

Goals For This Week

Content notes!

Weekly Planner!

Week Beginning: _____

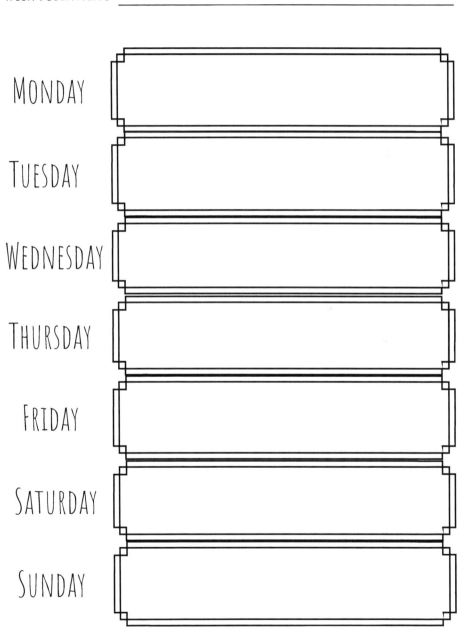

Monday

Tuesday

Wednesday

Thursday

Friday

Saturday

Sunday

Priority Tasks

Little Extras

Goals For This Week

CONTENT NOTES!

Weekly Planner!

Week Beginning: _____

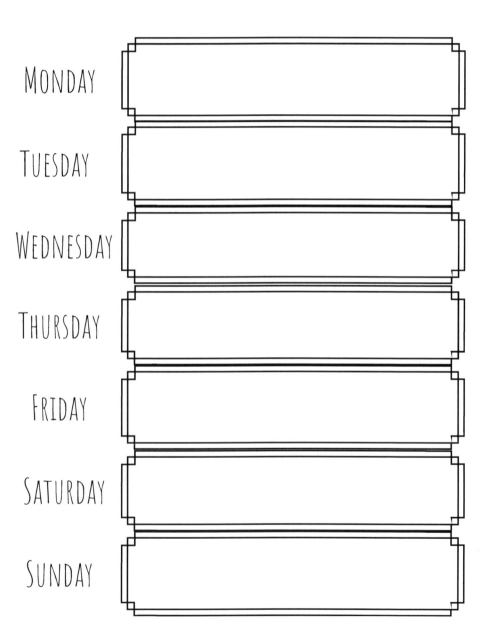

Monday

Tuesday

Wednesday

Thursday

Friday

Saturday

Sunday

Priority Tasks

Little Extras

Goals For This Week

CONTENT NOTES!

Weekly Planner!

Week Beginning: _____

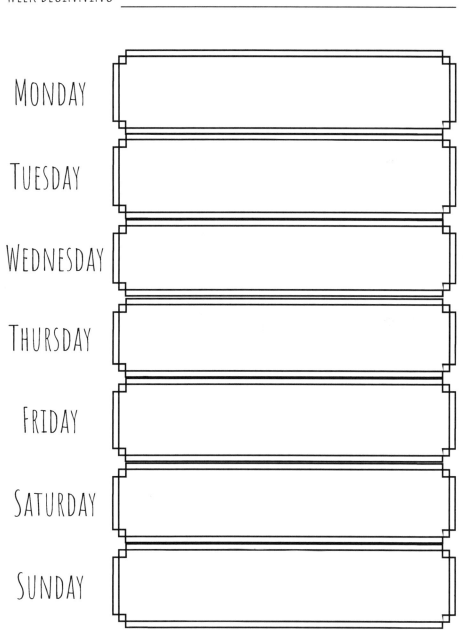

Monday

Tuesday

Wednesday

Thursday

Friday

Saturday

Sunday

Priority Tasks

Little Extras

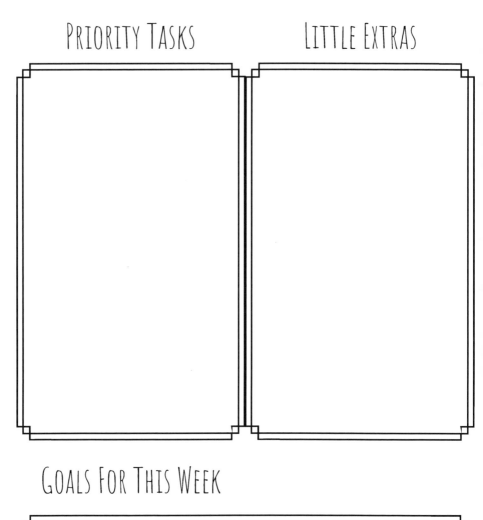

Goals For This Week

CONTENT NOTES!

Weekly Planner!

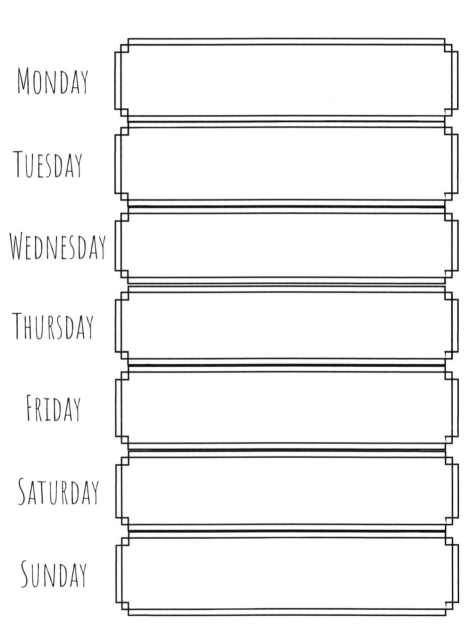

Monday

Tuesday

Wednesday

Thursday

Friday

Saturday

Sunday

Priority Tasks

Little Extras

Goals For This Week

CONTENT NOTES!

WHAT AN AMAZING YEAR!

Time to reflect on the best bits of my content creation journey this past year! What am I most proud of?

_____

_____

_____

_____

_____

_____

_____

_____

_____

_____

_____

_____

_____

_____

_____

_____

_____

I CAN'T WAIT TO SEE WHAT THE NEXT YEAR BRINGS!

Made in the USA
Columbia, SC
18 July 2023